This book belongs to

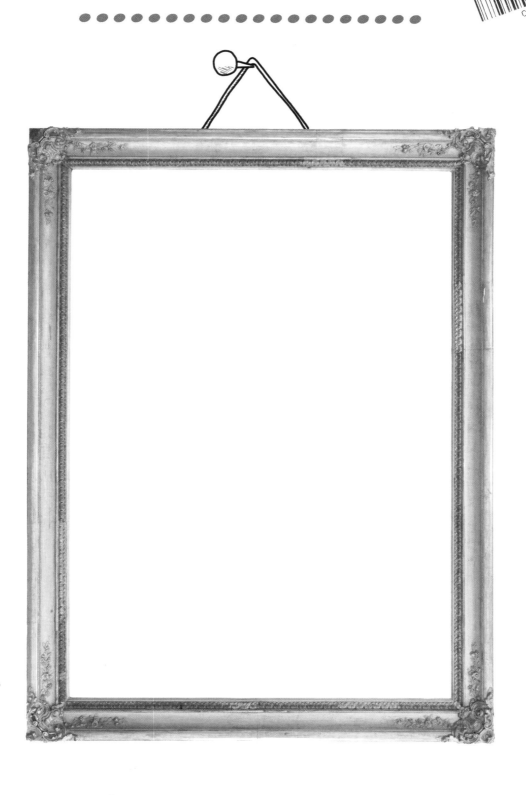

Draw a picture
of yourself.

COLOUR THE DINOSAURS IN.

Doodlepedia
DINOSAURS

The FUN and CRAZY world of DINOSAURS, DOODLING FUN, and ROARING FACTS

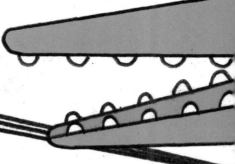

LONDON, NEW YORK, MELBOURNE, MUNICH, AND DELHI

Editor James Mitchem
Senior Designer Sadie Thomas
Designer Ria Holland
Text by James Mitchem
Consultant Darren Naish
Illustrators Emma Atkinson, Carolyn Bayley,
Holly Blackman, Helen Dodsworth, Chris Howker,
Barney Ibbotson, Evan Nave, Peter Todd,
Dan Woodger, Jay Wright, Jake McDonald
Jacket Designer Jess Bentall
Jacket Illustrator Holly Blackman
Managing Editor Penny Smith
Managing Art Editor Marianne Markham
Art Director Jane Bull
Category Publisher Mary Ling
Producer, Pre-Production Andy Hilliard
Senior Producer Seyhan Esen
Creative Technical Support Sonia Charbonnier

First published in Great Britain in 2013 by
Dorling Kindersley Limited,
80 Strand, London, WC2R 0RL

Copyright© 2013 Dorling Kindersley Limited
A Penguin Company
10 9 8 7 6 5 4 3 2
005 – 187178 – 08/13

A CIP catalogue record for this book is available from
the British Library
ISBN: 978-1-4093-6474-0
Printed and bound in China by Leo Paper Products Ltd.

Discover more at www.dk.com

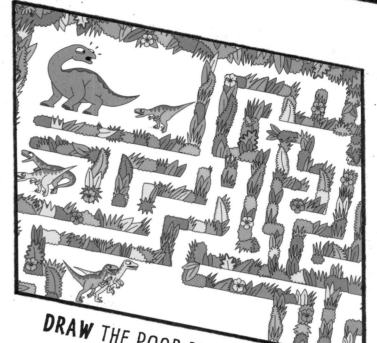

DRAW THE POOR DINOSAUR A SAFE
ROUTE OUT OF THE MAZE.

FIND AND **COLOUR** THE DIFFERENT
TYPES OF SAUROPOD.

Doodlepedia
DINOSAURS

The FUN and CRAZY world of DINOSAURS,
DOODLING FUN, and ROARING FACTS

DISCOVER THE DIFFERENT PERIODS OF
THE DINOSAUR AGE.

LEARN WHY THE DINOSAURS
BECAME EXTINCT.

DOODLE MORE DINOS IN THE EMPTY BOX.

DOODLEPEDIA
is exactly what it says on the cover – a book of doodling! Colour, design, and draw all over the pages and learn as you create. Find out about dinosaurs, pterosaurs, marine reptiles, and lots more! Are you ready for oodles of doodling fun? Then turn the page and begin!

Megatooth
If you thought plesiosaurs were scary, you're in for a shock. Megatooth (**MEG-a-tooth**), an ancestor of the great white shark, may have existed 40 million years after the time of the dinosaurs, pterosaurs, and marine reptiles, but it was the all-time **ultimate monster of the deep**. It grew to up to 20m (67ft) long, weighed up to 100 tonnes, and is probably the most ferocious predator ever.

Ahh! I'm getting out of here!!

START

FINISH

DRAW A WAY OUT OF THE MEGATOOTH MAZE.

DRAW A PATH OUT OF THE MEGATOOTH MAZE.

Crests and plumes
Many dinosaurs had impressive crests and plumes on their heads to **attract mates** and to **threaten rivals**. They came in all shapes and sizes. Can you imagine what they might look like?

PARASAUROLOPHUS

CRYOLOPHOSAURUS

DRAW CRESTS AND PLUMES ON THE DINOSAURS, THEN MAKE UP YOUR OWN AND

GUANLONG

FINISH THE DINOSAUR'S CRESTS.

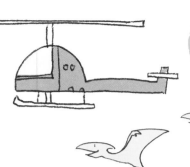

LEARN
WHAT FOOD CARNIVORES ATE.

Carnivores

While the majority of dinosaurs happily munched on plants, carnivores (meat-eaters) survived by eating lizards, insects, and other dinosaurs. Although many carnivores had similar dining habits, they were often very different. For example, Compsognathus (COMP-sog-NAITH-us), was only the size of a chicken, and scavenged a lot of its meals, but the monstrous Carnotaurus (CAR-no-TAWR-us) was about twice as big as a man. Imagine how much it would need to eat to get full up!

DRAW A MEAL FOR THE HUNGRY CARNOTAURUS.

Carnivores had large hearts and lungs which helped them get lots of oxygen. This made it easier for them to hunt! Remember, their dinner could run away from them!

Smaller carnivores sometimes had to **scavenge** for their meat.

Pterosaurs

Pterosaurs (teh-ROH-saw) weren't dinosaurs, but were flying creatures that ruled the skies in the age of the dinosaurs. They were the first **vertebrates** (animals with backbones) to fly. Ranging in size from sparrows to aeroplanes, the biggest pterosaurs were the biggest animals ever known to fly. They **terrorized** the skies, swooping over the sea, scooping up fish and other sea creatures, or scavenging for food on land.

COLOUR THE
DIFFERENT TYPES OF PTEROSAUR.

COLOUR ALL THE SORDES GREEN.

COLOUR ALL THE TUPANDACTYLUS YELLOW.

COLOUR ALL THE GERMANODACTYLUS BLUE.

COLOUR ALL THE PTERODACTYLUS PURPLE.

COLOUR ALL THE DORYGNATHUS RED.

What is a dinosaur?

Long before humans existed, dinosaurs ruled the Earth. For millions of years these amazing reptiles thrived. Dinosaurs came in all shapes and sizes, and there's still so much we don't know about them. In fact, it's very likely there are new and interesting species we haven't even discovered yet. One thing is for sure though – they were all amazing!

DESIGN YOUR OWN DINOSAURS.

Dinosaurs can be split into two categories: **ornithischians** (bird-hipped), and **saurischians** (lizard-hipped).

They all had **scaly skin,** but some of them also had **feathers.**

Most dinosaurs ate plants, but many were **meat-eaters**

Many dinosaurs were huge, others were small.

Some walked on **two legs**, others walked on **four.**

All dinosaurs had **tails.**

All dinosaurs had **clawed or hooved** hands and feet.

The Mesozoic world

If you travelled back in time to see the rise of the dinosaurs, you'd need to go back about 250 million years to a period of Earth's history called the **Mesozoic Era**. Back then, the Earth was **very different**, and all of the continents were joined together in one big super-continent called **Pangaea**, which means "All Earth". The Mesozoic Era was divided into three periods: the Triassic, the Jurassic, and the Cretaceous. Each of these periods had its own climate and wildlife.

Because the Mesozoic era was so long, dinosaurs from different periods would have **never met**. In fact, more time separates Stegosaurus from T. rex, than T. rex from us!

DRAW A PICTURE OF YOURSELF IN THE TIME MACHINE.

Herrerasaurus

Coelophysis

Lesothosaurus

TRIASSIC
(251–200 MILLION YEARS AGO).

Mussaurus

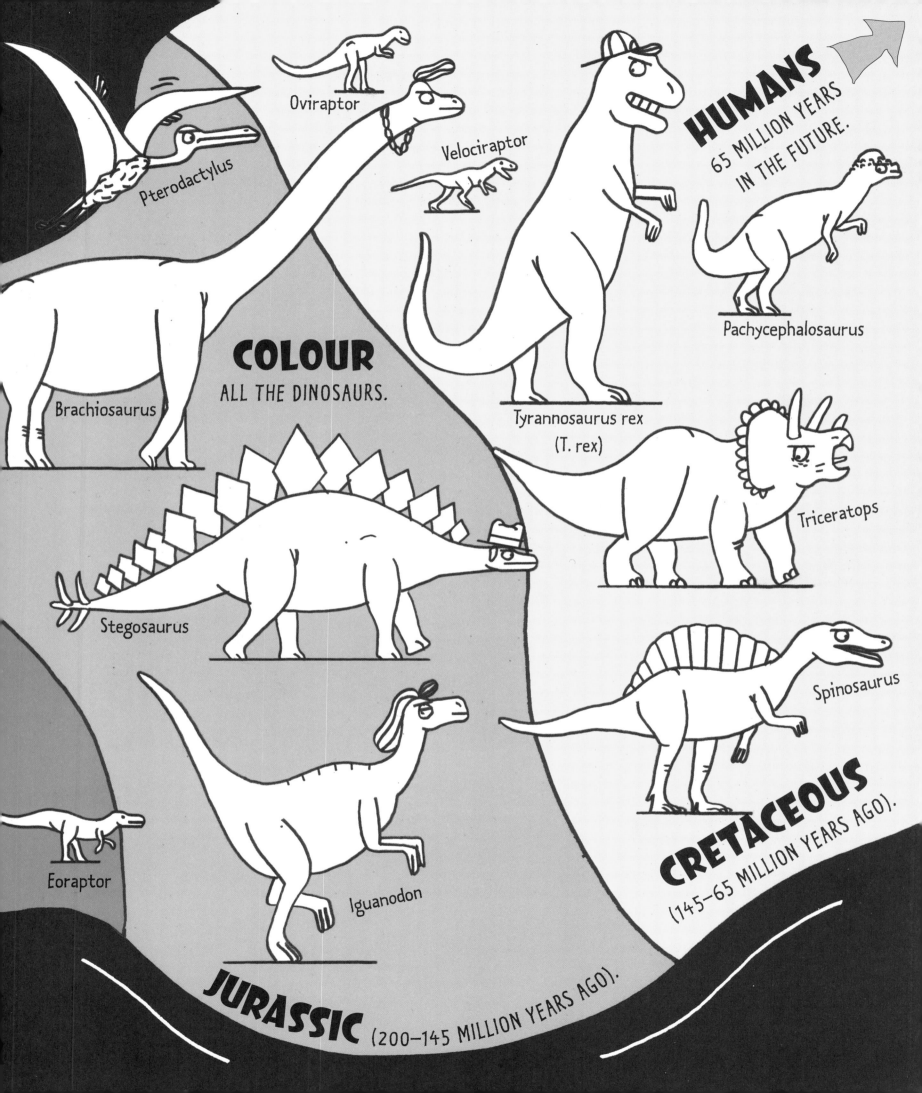

The Earth was very **dry** during the Triassic period. Only the coast and valleys saw much water.

FINISH THE REST
OF THE TRIASSIC SCENE.

Herrerasaurus

Eoraptor

GRRR

We don't have any photos to show us what life was like back then. Everything we know, we learn from **studying the remains** of prehistoric things (fossils).

Plateosaurus

The Triassic period

The Earth's scenery was very different during the **Triassic period** (between 251–200 million years ago). It was very hot and the land was covered in large patches of desert, with no grass or flowers, and only a few plants. It was during the early Triassic period that the first dinosaurs, such as the Eoraptor **(EE-oh-rap-tor)**, Plateosaurus **(PLATE-ee-oh-SORE-us)**, and Herrerasaurus **(her-RARE-uh-SAWR-us)** first emerged.

The Jurassic period

By the time the Triassic period ended 200 million years ago, the Earth had **changed dramatically**. The supercontinent Pangaea **split apart**, creating new continents, oceans, and seas. This meant that the planet's temperature cooled, causing **deserts to shrink, and lush forests to grow**. These changes created a lot more food for wildlife. As a result, the Jurassic period saw many **new species** of dinosaur appear.

COLOUR THE DINOSAURS IN.

It was during the Jurassic period that the stout Stegosaurus (**STEG-oh-SORE-uss**), the fierce Allosaurus (**al-oh-SORE-us**), and the super-sized Brachiosaurus (**brackee-oh-SORE-uss**) existed.

The Cretaceous period

The longest period of the Mesozoic Era was the Cretaceous, which spanned from 145–65 million years ago. It was a time of **incredible diversity**, when many new species of dinosaurs appeared. One reason for this was that the continents that formed when Pangaea split drifted farther apart, **spreading dinosaurs to new corners of the Earth.** At the time, the continents were still different to the way they are today, but they started to look more like they do now.

North America

Europe

Asia

Africa

South America

Australia

Antarctica

COLOUR
THE CONTINENTS AND TRY TO MATCH EACH MODERN VERSION.

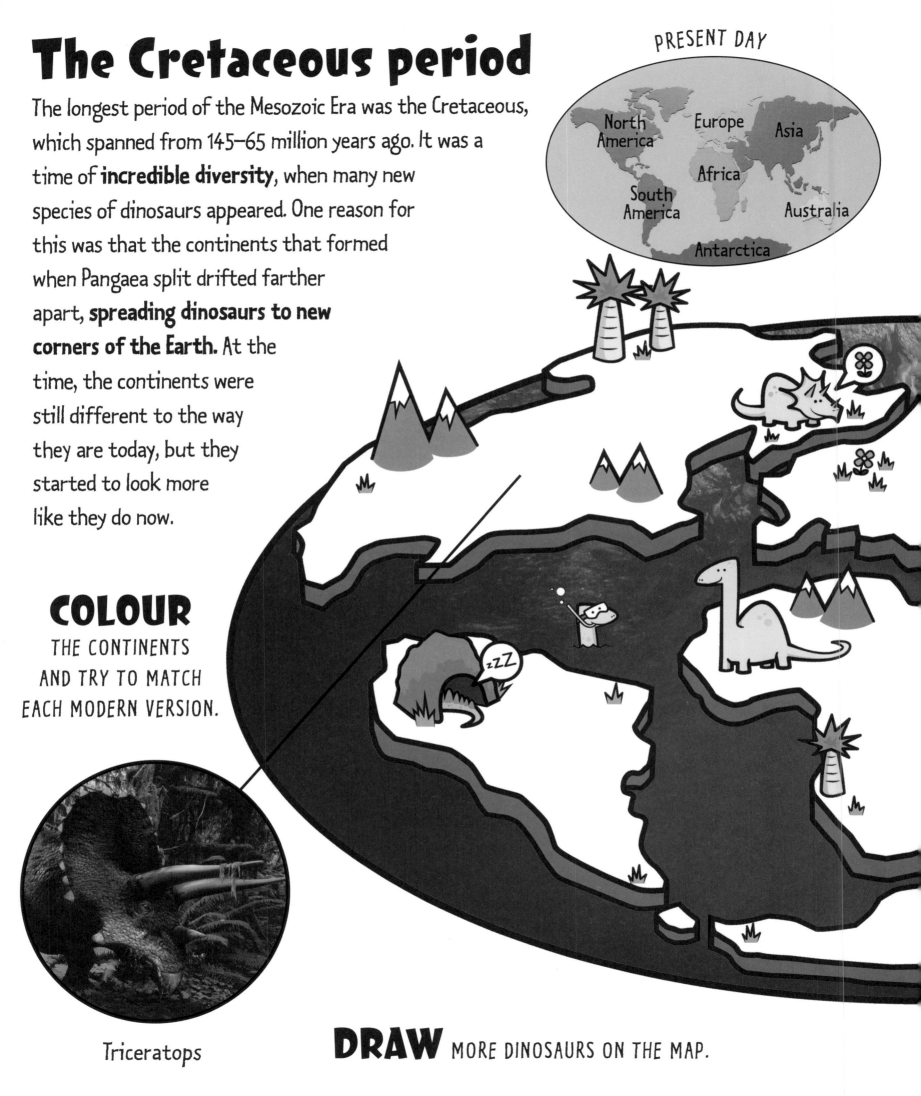

Triceratops

DRAW MORE DINOSAURS ON THE MAP.

The Cretaceous period was when some of the most well known dinosaurs existed, including Tyrannosaurus rex, Triceratops, and Velociraptor.

Earth's continents are still moving today, just very slowly!

Tyrannosaurus rex

Herbivores

The word dinosaur means "terrible lizard", but that doesn't mean they were all terrible! It's true many dinosaurs were predators, but most were actually **plant-eaters** (herbivores). By the time the Jurassic period rolled around, the Earth was covered with forests – or to a herbivore, **free dinner** for the taking! They just had to get there before all the other dinosaurs showed up!

The biggest dinosaurs of all, sauropods, only ate plants. They had to graze **all day** to get enough fuel. It's amazing there was enough to go around!

DRAW MORE DINOSAURS GETTING THEIR DINNER.

CYCADS

BABY GINGKOS

FERNS

DRAW FOOD IN THE DINOSAUR'S BASKETS BEFORE IT'S ALL GONE!

Carnivores

While the majority of dinosaurs happily munched on plants, carnivores (meat-eaters) survived by eating lizards, insects, and other dinosaurs. Although many carnivores had similar dining habits, they were often very different. For example, Compsognathus (**COMP-sog-NAITH-us**), was only the size of a chicken, and scavenged a lot of its meals, but the monstrous Carnotaurus (**CAR-no-TAWR-us**) was about twice as big as a man. Imagine how much it would need to eat to get full up!

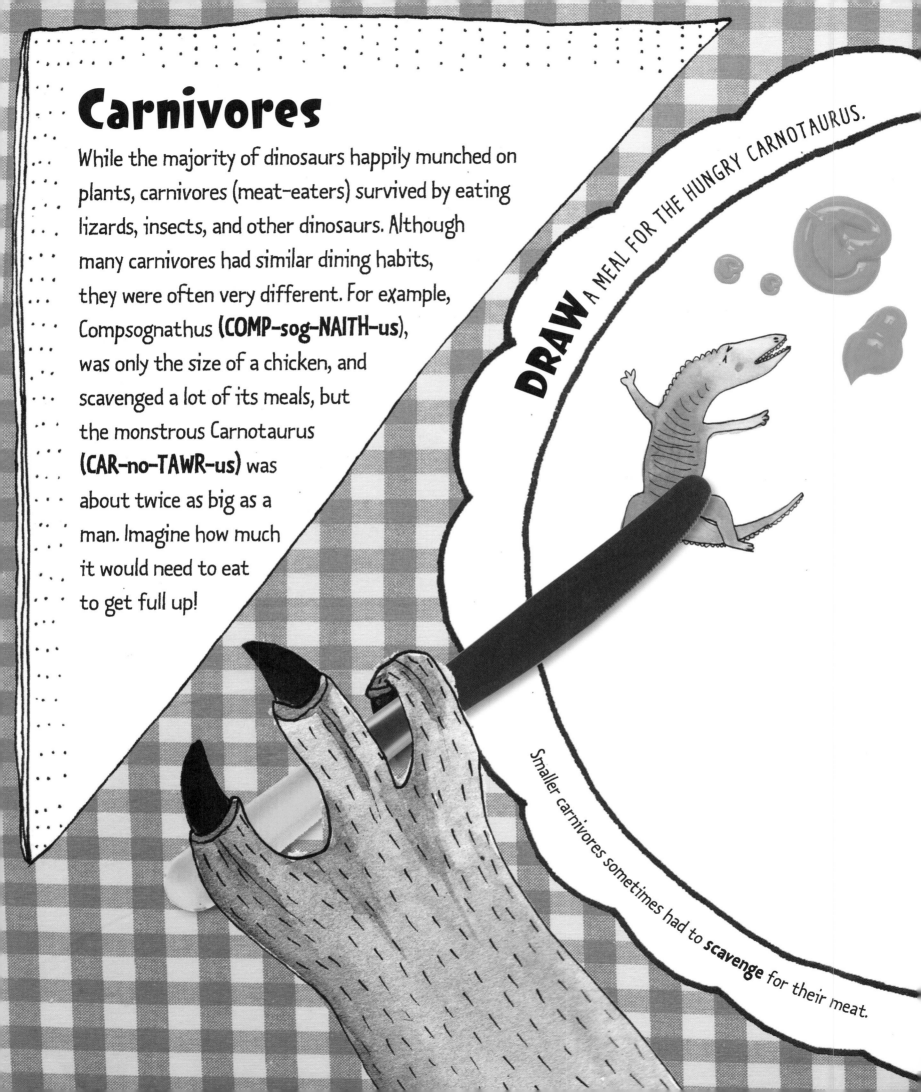

DRAW A MEAL FOR THE HUNGRY CARNOTAURUS.

Smaller carnivores sometimes had to **scavenge** for their meat.

Carnivores had large hearts and lungs which helped them get lots of oxygen. This made it easier for them to hunt! Remember, their dinner could run away from them!

SAVE THE TENONTOSAURUS.
DRAW A SAFE ROUTE OUT OF THE FOREST.

START

Pack attack

Not all predators were big, and sometimes they were **smaller than their prey**. (Imagine your dinner being bigger than you!) To turn the tables, dinosaurs such as Deinonychus **(dye-NON-ee-cuss)** would hunt prey that had been separated from its **herd**, and gang up before moving in for the kill.

FINISH

Deinonychus and
Velociraptor were among
the deadliest pack hunters.

COLOUR

THE FOREST AND
CAMOUFLAGE THE
SCUTELLOSAURUS.

Habitats

The world the dinosaurs lived in was very different to ours. Dinosaurs lived in all sorts of **environments**, and were always looking for the right place to call **home**.

COLOUR THE DESERT.

Deserts – the Earth's climate was **warmer** than it is today, and large areas of desert were found throughout the Mesozoic era.

DRAW MORE DINOSAURS OCCUPYING THE SCRUBLAND.

Scrubland – This **semi-desert** supported plants that didn't require much water to survive, and was home for many early species of dinosaur.

FINISH THE REST OF THE MOUNTAIN RANGE.

Mountains – These appeared at a growing rate as the Earth's **plates shifted** over the years, but it's likely there wasn't a great deal of food there.

Swampland – Swamps were very common throughout the Cretaceous, and were home to **hadrosaurs** and many other herbivores.

Riverbanks – All living things need water to survive, so a lot of dinosaurs settled close to **riverbanks** and **coasts**.

FINISH THE FOREST AND **DRAW** ANOTHER TRICERATOPS.

Forests – Even though dense forests would have helped predators to blend in, they were a **rich source of food** for herbivores such as Triceratops **(try-SERRA-tops)**.

Therizinosaurus

Small head

Lethal claws

ROLL UP ROLL UP

Feathers

Potbelly

It's easy to see why Therizinosaurus was nicknamed **"scythe lizard"**. Its monstrous claws were almost 1m (3ft) long.

Stumpy feet

The strangest dinosaur had to be Therizinosaurus (**THERRY-zin-oh-SORE-us**). When scientists studied the fossils, they couldn't believe how unusual it was. They stood on their back legs like most predators, but they only ate plants. They had lethal claws, but didn't use them for hunting. They had small heads, feathers, stumpy feet, and their large digestive systems meant they had big **potbellies!** How weird!

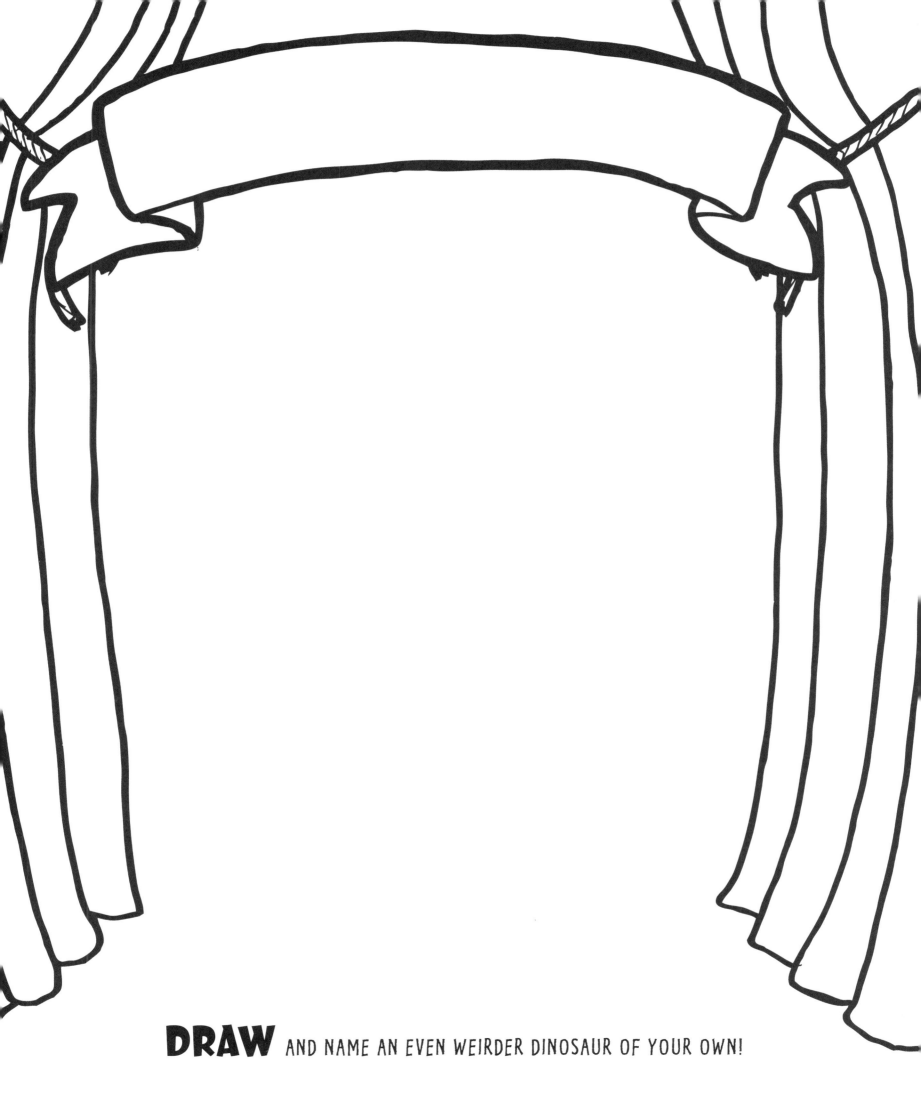

DRAW AND NAME AN EVEN WEIRDER DINOSAUR OF YOUR OWN!

Crests and plumes

Many dinosaurs had impressive crests and plumes on their heads to **attract mates** and to **threaten rivals**. They came in all shapes and sizes. Can you imagine what they might look like?

PARASAUROLOPHUS

Guanlong **(GWON-long),** an early relative of Tyrannosaurus rex, was discovered in China in 2006.

GUANLONG

CRYOLOPHOSAURUS

DRAW CRESTS AND PLUMES ON THE DINOSAURS, THEN MAKE UP YOUR OWN AND GIVE THEM NAMES.

Sticking together

If you were a herbivore, danger could be lurking around every corner. Plant-eaters such as Tenontosaurus **(ten-NON-toe-SORE-us)** that weren't able to defend themselves, looked for **safety in numbers** and travelled in herds to make sneaky predators think twice about attacking them.

Modern animals such as zebras and wildebeests travel in herds for the same reason.

FINISH AND **COLOUR** THE REST OF THE HERD.

Bone dome

Pachycephalosaurus (PACK-ee-sef-ah-low-SORE-us) was famous for a very unusual feature. They had a huge, thick skull shaped a little like a **bowling ball**, which might look ugly, but don't tell them that! Experts believe they used it like a **battering ram** to discourage predators and to intimidate rivals, similar to how stags butt heads today. However, it's also possible that it was just for show.

The dome was made of **solid bone**, and was 25cm (10in) thick!

The word pachycephalosaur means "thick-headed lizard".

Walking weapons

Danger was everywhere during the time of the dinosaurs — even predators were sometimes **prey for bigger dinosaurs themselves!** Only the biggest and strongest such as Tyrannosaurus rex could feel safe at all times. The scariest predators didn't need any special weapons to take down their prey — they had their own!

T. rex's jaw was so powerful that it could **crush the bones** of its prey with ease.

Allosaurus had a weak jaw, but very sharp teeth. It's possible it **slashed** its prey rather than try to bite it.

Many types of **raptor** had claws so sharp that their prey wouldn't have stood a chance against them.

DRAW YOUR OWN DINOSAURS WITH DEADLY WEAPONS.

Defence

No dinosaur wanted to be an easy meal. Some would try to fight off predators with their claws and teeth, but others – such as a group of dinosaurs called **ankylosaurs** – had special defensive features such as plates and spines. One of which was Euoplocephalus **(YOU-owe-plo-SEFF-ah-luss)**, which was **built like a tank**, and had a crushing club made of bone at the end of its tail, that it would swing at attacking predators.

Euoplocephalus was so armoured with spikes and plates, that even its **eyelids** were protected!

DESIGN YOUR OWN ARMOURED DINOSAUR.

FIGHTING BACK

When under attack from predators, dinosaurs were faced with a choice: to either **run or fight**. And sometimes the best defence was a good offence. Several herbivores had more than just armour, and were equipped with deadly weapons of their own to help them **fight back** against their enemies.

STEGOSAURUS

Stegosaurus had **razor sharp** spikes on its tail, which it could whip at enemies.

PENTACERATOPS

Pentaceratops and other ceratopsians could use their large **horns** as weapons of defence.

IGUANODON

Iguanodon had sharp **spikes** on its hands to jab at attackers.

DIPLODOCUS

Aside from being huge, Diplodocus could use its long tail like a **whip**.

DRAW THE FIGHTING DINOSAURS.

FINISH
DRAWING THE
SPINES ON
THE DINOSAURS.

OURANOSAURUS

RAYOSOSAURUS

Spines and sails

It wasn't just their teeth and claws that
helped dinosaurs stand out. Several dinosaurs
had sail-like spines on their backs and necks.
While these would have mainly been used to
attract mates and **scare off rivals**, experts
believe that they might also have helped
dinosaurs manage their body temperature.

SPINOSAURUS

One of the most impressive spines belonged to **Spinosaurus**, the largest predator to ever walk the Earth. It was **even bigger** than Tyrannosaurus rex!

Mini monster

Who says you had to be big to be a predator? Compsognathus (**COMP-sog-NAITH-us**), a predator from the Jurassic period, was no bigger than a **chicken**! It used its speed and agility to chase down fast-moving lizards and insects, scavenge other predators' kills, and even sometimes **gang up** and take on larger prey.

It may be small, but it was fast. Despite its size, Compsognathus could **run at speeds of more than 40kph** (25mph).

40

DRAW

THE REST OF THE
COMPSOGNATHUS PACK.

Compsognathus may have
been covered in **feathers,
fuzz,** or **scales** to help
it keep warm.

Grazing giants

The Jurassic saw the rise of the sauropods – the largest creatures to ever walk the Earth. The largest of these, Argentinosaurus **(ARE-jen-teen-oh-SORE-us)**, grew to up to 36m (118ft) long, and weighed as much as **13 elephants**. It would have needed to eat all day to have the energy to move!

A single Brachiosaurus would need to eat around 180kg of food **every day!**

COLOUR THE ARGENTINOSAURUS GREEN.

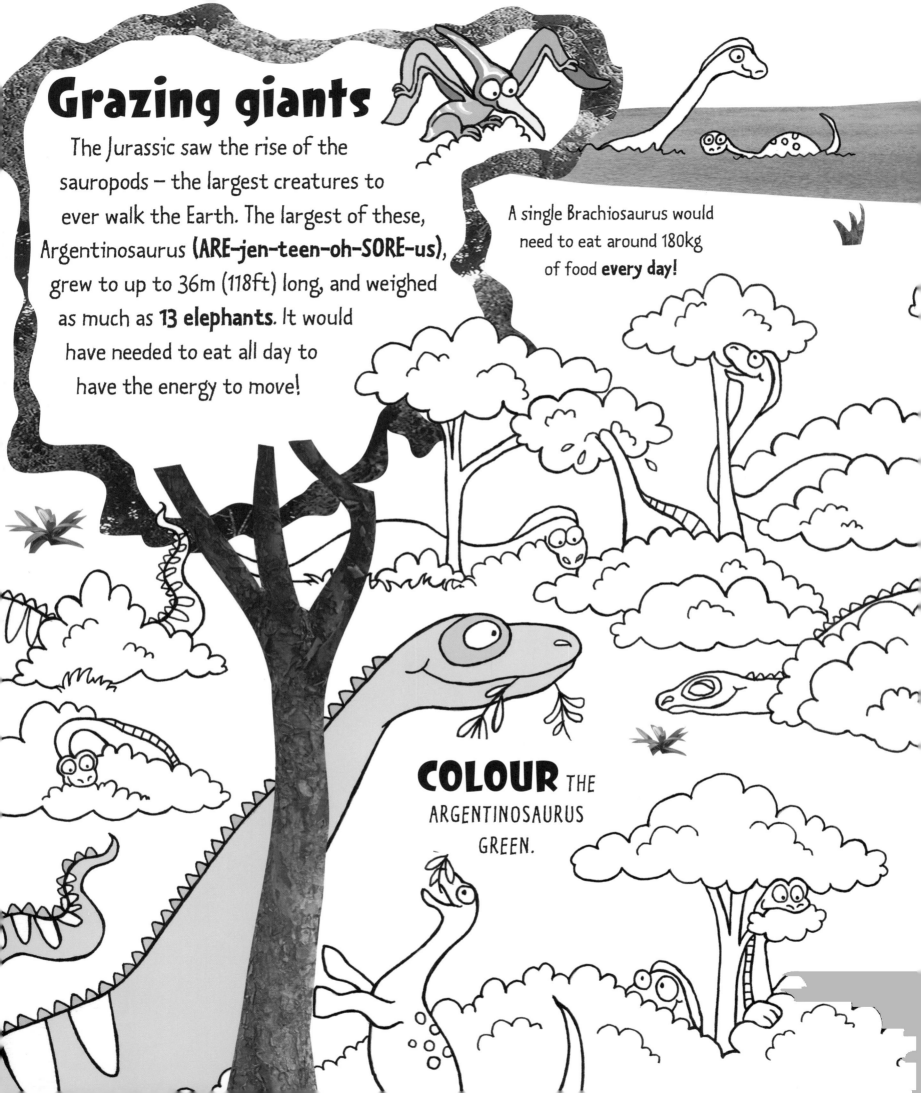

COLOUR

THE DIPLODOCUS RED.

Sauropods had long necks so they reach food other dinosaurs couldn't. Some could even stand up on their **hind legs**!

Sauropods were plant-eaters, but that doesn't mean they couldn't defend themselves from predators. They were so massive that they could **crush** any attackers.

COLOUR THE
BRACHIOSAURUS YELLOW.

COLOUR THE
SALTASAURUS BLUE.

Titans of the Earth

Tyrannosaurus rex gets all the glory, but there were plenty of other giant predators around. In fact, T. rex's "cousin" Giganotosaurus **(gig-AN-oh-toe-SORE-rus)** was just as big. It's lucky they lived 10 million years apart, or there would have been **nasty fights** over their dinner!

Experts believe that Giganotosaurus had a brain the shape of a **banana!**

No complete Giganotosaurus skeleton has ever been found, but experts believe they were about 13.5m (45ft) long, and would have weighed as much as **125 people!**

COLOUR THE GIGANOTOSAURUS BLUE.

COLOUR THE CARNOTAURUS RED.

COLOUR THE TYRANNOSAURUS GREEN.

COLOUR THE TYRANNOTITANS YELLOW.

COLOUR THE CARCHARODONTOSAURUS PURPLE.

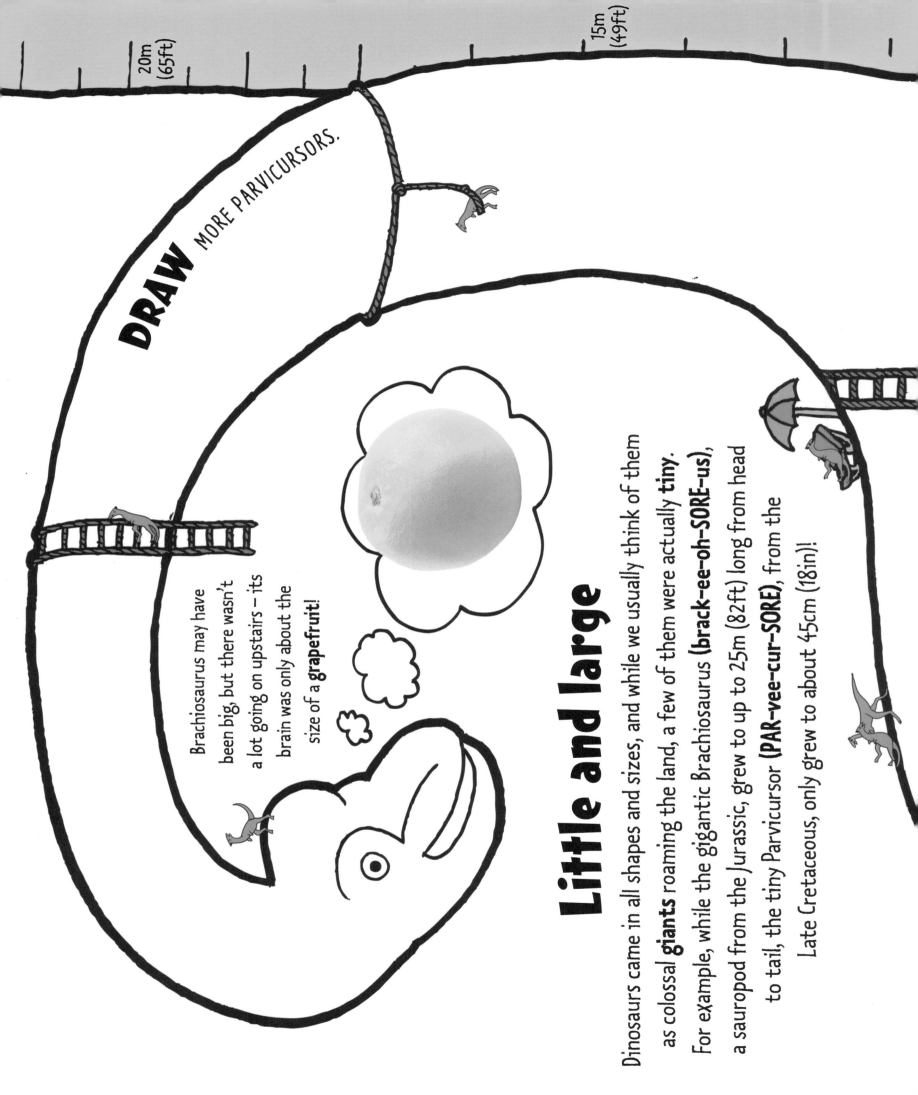

DRAW MORE PARVICURSORS.

Brachiosaurus may have been big, but there wasn't a lot going on upstairs – its brain was only about the size of a **grapefruit!**

Little and large

Dinosaurs came in all shapes and sizes, and while we usually think of them as colossal **giants** roaming the land, a few of them were actually **tiny**.

For example, while the gigantic Brachiosaurus (**brack-ee-oh-SORE-us**), a sauropod from the Jurassic, grew to up to 25m (82ft) long from head to tail, the tiny Parvicursor (**PAR-vee-cur-SORE**), from the Late Cretaceous, only grew to about 45cm (18in)!

Parvicursors had a fairly large claw on each hand, but they were probably for **digging** rather than defending themselves.

Fast and slow

Fossils give us clues about how fast dinosaurs could run. It varied between species, and while no dinosaur was as fast as the fastest modern land animal, the **cheetah**, which can run at **114kph** (70mph), smaller dinosaurs could probably reach very fast speeds. Others, such as the giant sauropods were very slow.

Brachiosaurus weighed so much that it probably couldn't move faster than 6kph (3.5mph)!

Ankylosaurus was built like a tank, so it **didn't need to** run away from predators, so it was probably slow-moving.

Ankylosaurus

Brachiosaurus

DRAW MORE RACING DINOSAURS.

Predators walked on two legs to be able to move fast enough to catch their food.

Predator and prey

In order to survive, all dinosaurs had to eat, and while herbivores were happy to chomp on plants, carnivores had something a little fresher in mind! Because of this, plant-eaters had to always be on the lookout for **hungry predators** ready to turn them into their next meal!

CAN YOU TELL THE HUNTERS FROM THE HUNTED? **COLOUR** THE PREDATORS ORANGE, AND THE PREY YELLOW.

Herbivores were slow-moving, and walked on four legs.

Stegosaurus

Don't let the fact that Stegosaurus **(STEG-oh-SORE-uss)** was a plant-eater trick you into thinking it was easy prey. It grew to up to 9m (30ft) long, and weighed **4 tonnes.** And with its impressive plates and **sharp spiky tail**, it was well equipped with the tools to fend off even the most fierce predators of the Jurassic period.

FINISH THE SPIKES ON THE TAIL.

Stegosaurus certainly wasn't the smartest dinosaur in the herd. Its brain was no bigger than a **walnut!**

Certain dinosaurs would **sit on their nests** the way that birds do.

START

Baby dinosaurs

Dinosaurs were reptiles, so scientists always thought that they probably laid eggs. But it wasn't until 1920, when the remains of the eggs and nests of a dinosaur called Oviraptor **(oh-vee-RAP-tor)** were found in the **Gobi Desert, China** that they could say for sure. This huge discovery helped scientists to understand much more about dinosaur life.

The temperature of dinosaur eggs could **determine the gender** of the babies. The warmer the eggs were, the more likely it was that they would hatch as males.

DRAW THE OVIRAPTOR A SAFE ROUTE BACK TO HER NEST.

FINISH

Oviraptor would sometimes dig its nests from sand or earth.

Parasaurolophus

During the Cretaceous, a group of dinosaurs called hadrosaurs, or "duck-billed" dinosaurs emerged. Among these was Parasaurolophus (**PA-ra-SORE-oh-LOAF-uss**) – a large plant-eater with hundreds of grinding teeth for mashing up food. They were common, and travelled in large herds, and are sometimes thought of as the dinosaur version of cows!

Unlike most other herbivores, hadrosaurs could walk on either two or four legs.

Parasaurolophus was **surprisingly big** for prey, and adults could grow to be 10m (33ft) long. No wonder it was a favourite meal for many carnivores – it made for very big portions!

CONNECT THE DOTS TO REVEAL THE PICTURE.

Nobody is certain if dinosaurs **communicated with sound**, but experts believe they probably did. One reason for this is that Parasaurolophus' crest contained a series of tubes that **connected to the nostrils** – which meant it might work like a trumpet.

Deinonychus

While teeth were the weapon of choice for many dinosaurs, others dealt damage with their **claws**. Perhaps the scariest of these dinosaurs was Deinonychus **(dye-NON-ee-cuss)**, a speedy pack hunter from the Early Cretaceous. As well as the sharp claws on its hands, Deinonychus had a monstrous upturned **sickle claw** on each foot that it used to deliver lethal strikes.

Deinonychus means "terrible claw" and it's easy to see why!

Deinonychus was lethal, but it was only 3m (10ft) long, so it roamed in packs to take down larger prey.

FINISH THE REST OF THE DEINONYCHUS PACK.

The long tail was held stiff to help with balance while running.

Dressed to frill

Known for their **horns** and neck frills, ceratopsians were a group of herbivores from the Cretaceous period. They might look scary, but their large frills and horns were **only for protection**, and their sharp beaks were used to **rip up plants** for food.

Although they look a little like them, ceratopsians have no link to the modern **rhinoceros**.

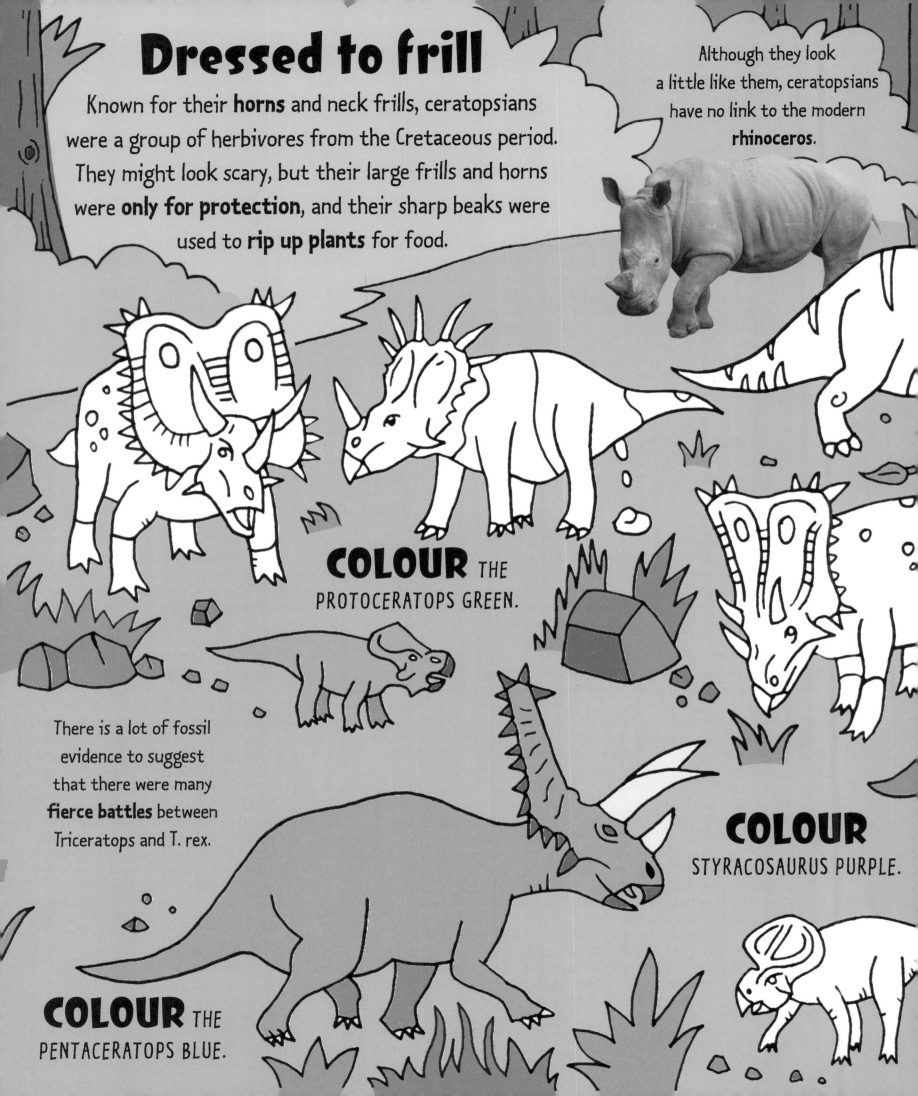

COLOUR THE PROTOCERATOPS GREEN.

There is a lot of fossil evidence to suggest that there were many **fierce battles** between Triceratops and T. rex.

COLOUR STYRACOSAURUS PURPLE.

COLOUR THE PENTACERATOPS BLUE.

Pentaceratops had a **giant skull** measuring 3m (10ft) long!

COLOUR THE TRICERATOPS RED.

COLOUR THE CHASMOSAURUS YELLOW.

The ultimate predator

Tyrannosaurus rex (**TIE-ran-oh-SORE-us**), or T. rex for short, was a ferocious hunter with a massive skull and **bone-crushing teeth**. At 4m (13ft) tall and 12m (40ft) long, it weighed as much as **five cars**. It was one of the biggest predators that ever lived, and terrorized the forests of what is now North America until it became extinct 65 million years ago. Phew!

FINISH THE T. REX'S DINNER INSIDE ITS STOMACH.

Pterosaurs

Pterosaurs (**teh-ROH-sores**) weren't dinosaurs, but were flying creatures that ruled the skies in the age of the dinosaurs. They were the first **vertebrates** (animals with backbones) to fly. Ranging in size from sparrows to aeroplanes, the biggest pterosaurs were the biggest animals ever known to fly. They **terrorized** the skies, swooping over the sea, scooping up fish and other sea creatures, or scavenging for food on land.

COLOUR THE SORDES GREEN.

COLOUR THE PTERODACTYLUS PURPLE.

COLOUR THE TUPANDACTYLUS YELLOW.

COLOUR THE GERMANODACTYLUS BLUE.

COLOUR THE DORYGNATHUS RED.

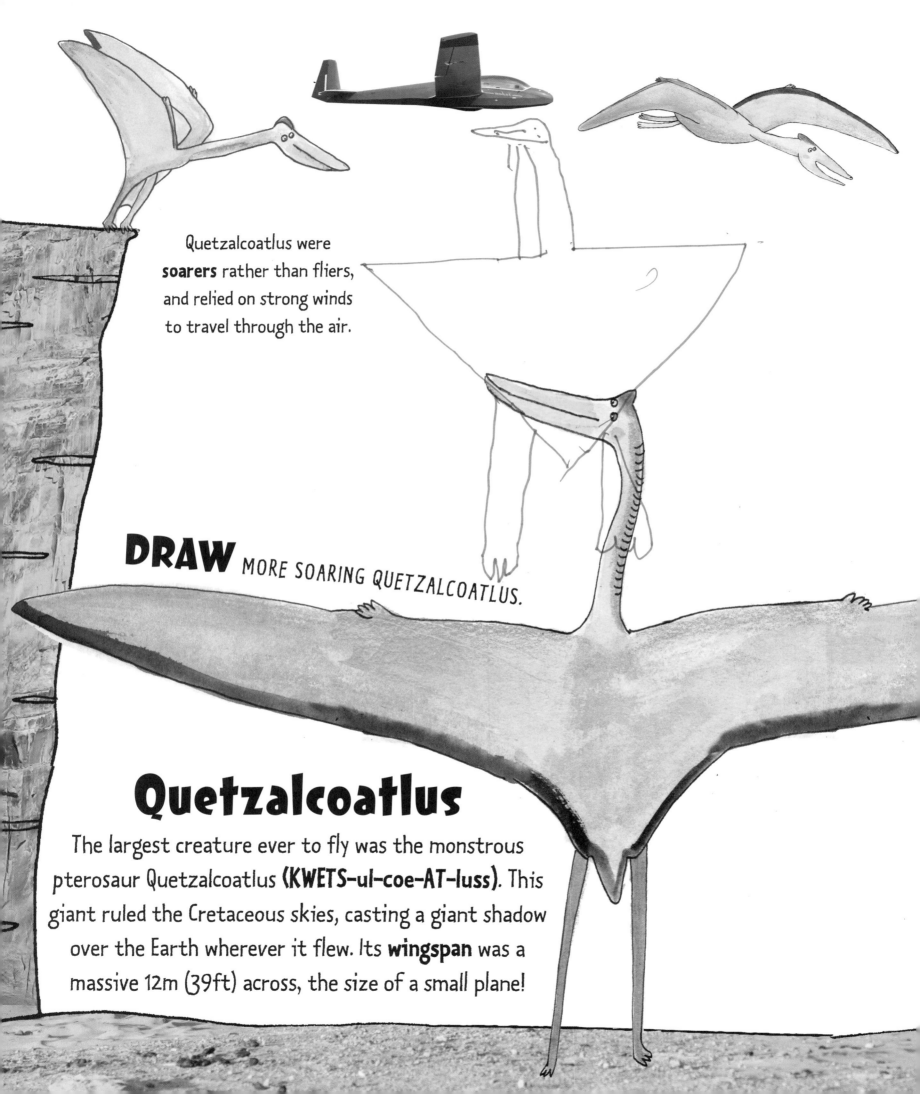

Quetzalcoatlus were **soarers** rather than fliers, and relied on strong winds to travel through the air.

DRAW MORE SOARING QUETZALCOATLUS.

Quetzalcoatlus

The largest creature ever to fly was the monstrous pterosaur Quetzalcoatlus **(KWETS-ul-coe-AT-luss)**. This giant ruled the Cretaceous skies, casting a giant shadow over the Earth wherever it flew. Its **wingspan** was a massive 12m (39ft) across, the size of a small plane!

How did something so big stay in the air? Quetzalcoatlus' bones were **hollow**, making it surprisingly light for its size.

WOAH!
Get me back to the 21st century!

The first bird

Believe it or not, birds are the descendants of dinosaurs. Technically, **they are** dinosaurs – the only surviving group! The earliest known bird is Archaeopteryx **(ar-kee-OP-ter-ix)**, which appeared in the Jurassic period. It had the feathered tail and wings of a bird, but the claws of a dinosaur.

COLOUR
IN THE FUNKY FEATHERS.

Archaeopteryx was about the same size as a modern raven.

Nobody knows
what colour their
feathers were.
For all we know
they could be
**bright pink
or orange!**

COLOUR THE TYLOSAURUS PURPLE.

COLOUR THE PLESIOSAURUS BLUE.

Creatures of the deep

Dinosaurs ruled the land, and pterosaurs dominated the sky, but it was **marine reptiles** that **lurked beneath the waves** during the Mesozoic Era. The largest of these massive monsters could grow up to 20m (70ft) long, and while they spent their lives in the water, they all **breathed air**.

The skull of Deinosuchus **(die-no-SUE-kus)** – a relative of modern crocodiles was 1.8m (6ft) long, and a fully grown Deinosuchus weighed up to 5 tonnes!

COLOUR THE DEINOSUCHUS YELLOW.

COLOUR THE ELASMOSAURUS RED.

Elasmosaurus had **72 bones** in its neck!

COLOUR THE KRONOSAURUS GREEN.

Rhomaleosaurus

The words "sea monsters" come to mind when you think of Rhomaleosaurus (ROME-alley-oh-SORE-us). They grew to up to 7m (21ft) long, and in many ways, were like the aquatic version of Tyrannosaurus rex. They **terrorized** the Jurassic seas, feasting on fish, squid, and smaller marine reptiles.

Rhomaleosaurus glided through the water using its four flippers like wings to **"fly"** underwater. Penguins and sea lions do a similar thing today.

CONNECT THE DOTS TO REVEAL THE PICTURE.

It's thought that like a lot of ocean predators, Rhomaleosaurus had a pale belly and dark back, making it **harder to spot** from both above and below.

Megatooth

If you thought plesiosaurs were scary, you're in for a shock. Megatooth **(MEG-a-tooth)**, an ancestor of the great white shark, may have existed 40 million years after the time of the dinosaurs, pterosaurs, and marine reptiles, but it was the all-time **ultimate monster of the deep**. It grew to up to 20m (67ft) long, weighed up to 100 tonnes, and is probably the most ferocious predator ever.

START

Megatooth's teeth were the size of dinner plates, and they had about **250** of them. That would take a lot of toothpaste to clean!

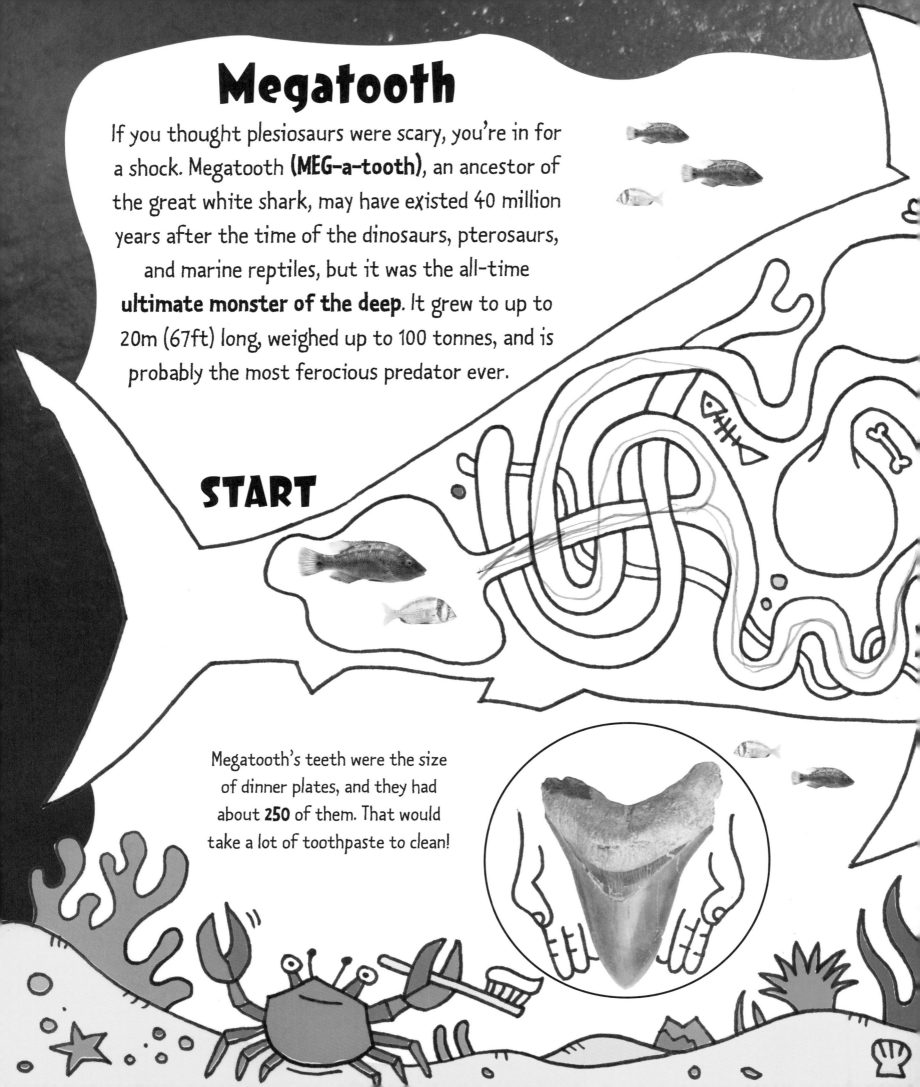

FINISH

DRAW A WAY OUT OF THE MEGATOOTH MAZE.

Great white shark

The ultimate beast!

All dinosaurs were amazing creatures, but some dinosaurs were a little more spectacular than others. These dinosaurs were among the **fastest, strongest, scariest, and most interesting** to have lived – but can you imagine what a dinosaur with all of these qualities combined would be like?

LONGEST NECK
MAMENCHISAURUS

PERIOD	JURASSIC
SIZE	★★★★★
SPEED	★
INTELLIGENCE	★★

BIGGEST BRAIN
TROODON

PERIOD	CRETACEOUS
SIZE	★
SPEED	★★★★
INTELLIGENCE	★★★★★

STRONGEST BITE
T. REX

PERIOD	CRETACEOUS
SIZE	★★★★
SPEED	★★★
INTELLIGENCE	★

DRAW THE SCARIEST DINOSAURS THAT NEVER LIVED BY COMBINING THE FEATURES OF THE OTHER DINOSAURS.

BEST ARMOUR
ANKYLOSAURUS

PERIOD	CRETACEOUS
SIZE	★★★
SPEED	★★
INTELLIGENCE	★★

DEADLIEST CLAWS
UTAHRAPTOR

PERIOD	CRETACEOUS
SIZE	★★★
SPEED	★★★★
INTELLIGENCE	★★★

FASTEST LEGS
STRUTHIOMIMUS

PERIOD	CRETACEOUS
SIZE	★★
SPEED	★★★★★
INTELLIGENCE	★★★★

Where did they go?

At the end of the Cretaceous period, dinosaurs were **thriving** like never before. Then, about 65 million years ago – with the exception of several species of bird – they **mysteriously died out**. The reason why this happened puzzled scientists for years, but they now believe that a **massive meteorite** crashed into the Earth. This caused earthquakes, tsunamis, volcanic eruptions, and threw up a cloud of dust so big that it blocked out the Sun.

In Mexico there is the **remains of a crater** 180km (112 miles) wide. Experts believe this is where the meteorite crash landed.

EEEK

DRAW MORE SCARED DINOSAURS!

Other theories about why the dinosaurs became extinct include an ice age, and a dinosaur **plague**.

Scientists estimate that the meteorite would have been roughly 10km (6 miles) wide, and struck the Earth at a **staggering** 100,000kph (62,000mph!)

THE DAILY DINO

WHAT SURVIVED?

In the millions of years that followed the destruction of the dinosaurs, many new species of animal **came and went**. However, a handful of creatures, other than birds from the Mesozoic Era, managed to **survive the extinction** and are still around today – on land, in the sea, and in the air.

SEE THE LATEST IN DINOSAUR FASHION!

DRAW THE REST OF THE SURVIVORS.

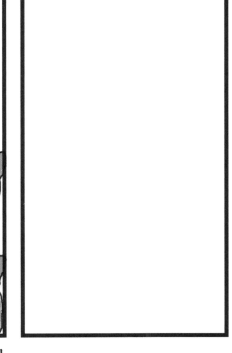

Various species of **fish, shark,** and **jellyfish** were among the creatures that survived in the seas.

It was only **small animals** such as lizards, insects, snakes, and crocodiles that survived on land.

While a lot of **early birds** became extinct, a few species managed to survive, and so did many flying insects.

FINISH

A MODERN CITY WITH PEOPLE AND DINOSAURS LIVING TOGETHER!

What if they weren't extinct?

In the years that followed the extinction caused by the meteorite, the world became a **very different** place. The continents shifted, the climate changed, and thousands of new species of animal and plant evolved. Eventually, human beings emerged and became the Earth's most **dominant species.** But can you imagine what the world would be like if the dinosaurs hadn't become extinct? Would we keep dinosaurs as pets? Or would they be destructive and try to eat us?

Turning to stone

Everything we know about dinosaurs, pterosaurs, and marine reptiles, we learned from their **fossilized remains**. Fossils are the stone remnants of things that lived long ago that have been preserved in the Earth's layers.

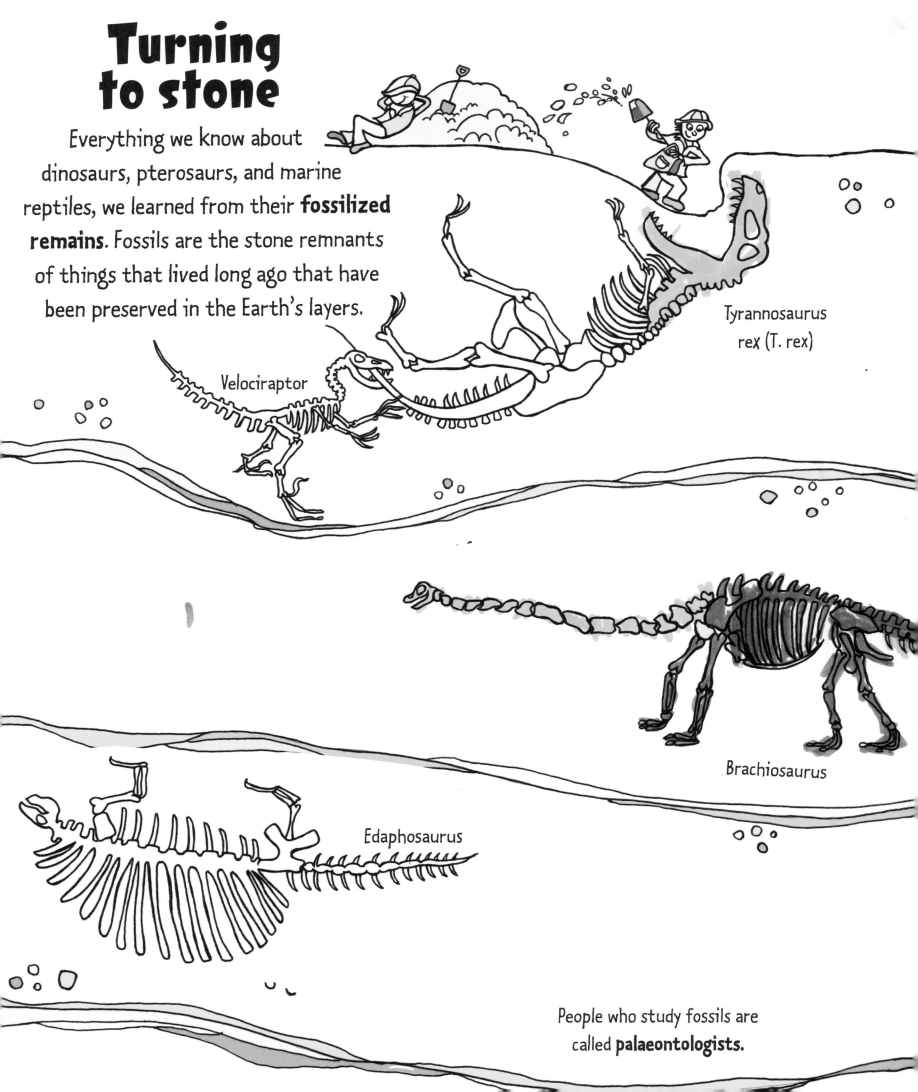

Tyrannosaurus rex (T. rex)

Velociraptor

Brachiosaurus

Edaphosaurus

People who study fossils are called **palaeontologists**.

Fossils are rare. Most dinosaurs simply decayed and **disappeared forever**. Only a few of the dinosaurs that lived have been, or will be, found as fossils.

Triceratops

Pterodactylus

DRAW MORE FOSSILS IN THE EARTH.

Fossilized eggs, feathers, footprints, and even **dinosaur poo** have been found. These all help us to understand more about prehistoric life.

Studying fossils

Not only are fossils **rare**, but they're also very fragile, and it takes a lot of hard work and patience for **palaeontologists** (fossil experts) to get them out of the ground. When a fossil is discovered, huge dig sites are set up, and it can take months before the fossils are fully excavated for study in a lab.

Fossils are usually encased in rock, so palaeontologists need a lot of tools to dig them out without breaking them.

FINISH THE OTHER HALF OF THE BURIED FOSSIL.

Dinosaurs on display

The dinosaurs might not be around anymore, but that shouldn't stop you from seeing what they were like. Museums have incredible dinosaur exhibits on display, including fossils that are **hundreds of millions** of years old, and even full skeletons!

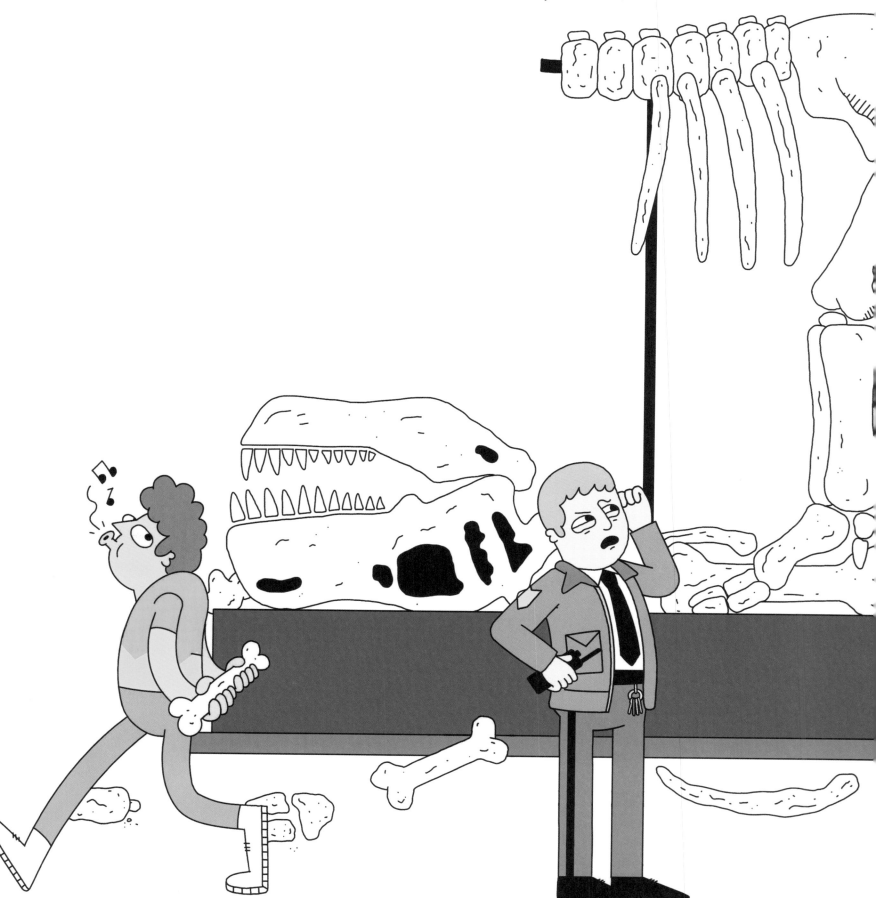

SOME OF THE T. REX BONES HAVE FALLEN OFF! **DRAW** THEM BACK ON TO FINISH THE DISPLAY.

"Sue" the T. rex fossil at the Field Museum, Chicago, USA is the most complete T-Rex fossil in the world. It cost the museum a whopping **£5.2 million ($8.4 million)** when they bought it in 1997.

TYRANNOSAURUS REX

Draw your own dinosaur

Now that you've learned all about these amazing creatures, draw **one of your own**. Who knows, one day a palaeontologist might discover one that looks just like it!

DESIGN, COLOUR AND NAME YOUR
OWN DINOSAUR.

DRAW SOMETHING PREHISTORIC TO COMPLETE THE BOOK.

DK WOULD LIKE TO THANK

The publisher would like to thank the following for their kind permission to reproduce their photographs:

Peter Minister for his Deinonychus image.

All other images © Dorling Kindersley
For further information see: www.dkimages.com